Dallas
Shapes Up!

Charles Hirsch
Illustrated by Bryan Liedahl

Rigby®

Tuesday, June 25

Tomorrow I'm flying to see Aunt Carola and Uncle Horacio for the first time since they moved from San Francisco, California, (where I live) to Dallas, Texas, two months ago. I'm too excited to sleep, so I'm writing in my journal. The three of us send e-mails to each other all the time, and sometimes we talk on the phone, yet I still miss them. The bank where Uncle Horacio works asked him to move, but if I could find a way to get them to move back, I'd be the happiest boy alive.

I take my camera with me everywhere so that I can photograph interesting things that I see.

Aunt Carola is on summer vacation from her job as a math teacher, so she'll be free to go exploring. In her last e-mail, she promised to show me all sorts of amazing things. I can't wait!

Uncle Horacio

Aunt Carola

Bernardo, that's me!

Aunt Carola has three favorite things in the whole world: baseball, seafood, and geometry. I love these things, too, so when she lived here in San Francisco, we would often go exploring to find examples of them. The first was easy to find: a Giants game at Pacific Bell Park! We'd jump up and down and cheer so loudly that we'd almost lose our voices. The second was easy to find, too. Almost every weekend, Aunt Carola and Uncle Horacio would take me to Fisherman's Wharf to eat crab enchiladas and watch the seals pop in and out of the ocean and bark at each other.

The cables on the Golden Gate Bridge run up and down, but they never cross each other. That's how I know that they're parallel.

The third thing, actually, was the easiest of all to find. When you're with Aunt Carola, geometric shapes seem to show up everywhere. We couldn't drive across the Golden Gate Bridge without hearing, "I see some **parallel lines**," or walk past the Transamerica Pyramid without her saying, "I see some triangular **faces**." Then I would have to find them, too.

But will our Dallas explorations be as much fun? I guess I'll find out soon.

I can see a triangular face on the Transamerica Pyramid.

Geometry Note

parallel lines — lines that do not cross and are always the same distance from each other

face — a flat side of a solid figure

Wednesday, June 26

When Aunt Carola met me at the airport this afternoon, she was surprised by how much I'd grown. But she looked just like I remembered her: sparkling brown eyes, neatly braided hair, and bright, colorful clothes. She has a whole closet full of outfits in different colors and patterns, and today she was wearing a bright yellow blouse with red triangles on it.

Back home there's usually a cool breeze blowing from the ocean, but here the air is hot and humid. When I stepped out of the air-conditioned airport into the bright Texas sun, I felt as if a warm, wet blanket were covering my skin.

As we drove to Aunt Carola's home, I tried to tell her all the news from home when, suddenly, I spotted a colorful building on the side of the road with an **obtuse angle** (larger than 90 degrees) over its entrance. I managed to snap its picture before we drove past.

The César Chávez Learning Center is not the school where Aunt Carola teaches, but many of the children in her neighborhood go there.

Geometry Note

obtuse angle   an angle larger than 90 degrees but smaller than 180 degrees

Aunt Carola and Uncle Horacio live in a gray brick building with an orange roof. Their apartment has only one bedroom, so I'll be sleeping on the foldout sofa. I'm really excited to have a room to myself for once (even if it's a living room). At home I share a bedroom with my older brother Gregorio, and the light from his bedside lamp always keeps me awake when he reads at night.

After I unpacked, Aunt Carola and I drove downtown to the West End Marketplace to meet Uncle Horacio for dinner. I thought for sure that we'd be eating seafood. Aunt Carola, however, said that we were going to a place where I'd feel right at home: a spaghetti restaurant with a real San Francisco trolley car where we could sit and eat!

It was dark when we left the restaurant, and I took a picture of some really neat, rainbow-colored lights that made bright **arcs** against the night sky. These shining, curved lines lit up our path as we walked back to the car.

It sure is great to be here with Aunt Carola and Uncle Horacio.

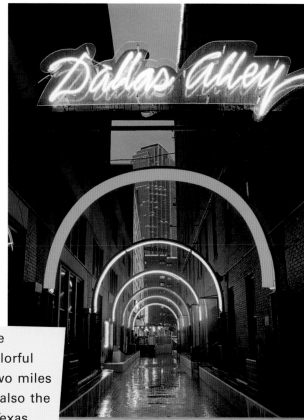

Aunt Carola says that the building behind these colorful arcs is lined with over two miles of green tube lights. It's also the third tallest building in Texas.

Geometry Note

arc 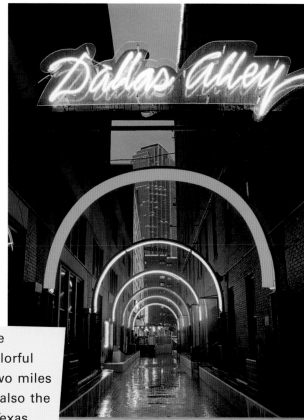 a curved line that forms part of a circle

Thursday, June 27

It's important that we *be* careful and put sunscreen on every day so that we don't get sunburned in the hot sunlight. After I'd finished smearing sunscreen on my arms, legs, and face this morning, Aunt Carola handed me a surprise: a map and a sheet of paper with written directions. My first direction was to find our starting point on the map—a grassy triangle with a **right angle** (90 degrees) and two **acute angles** (smaller than 90 degrees). I studied the map carefully as Aunt Carola drove toward downtown Dallas.

"Do I have to drive around in circles until you find the triangle, Bernardo?" she joked.

"No, we're going to Thanksgiving Square!" I shouted, finally locating a green triangle that fit her description.

Aunt Carola said that a city or town *square* can mean any open area where two streets meet.

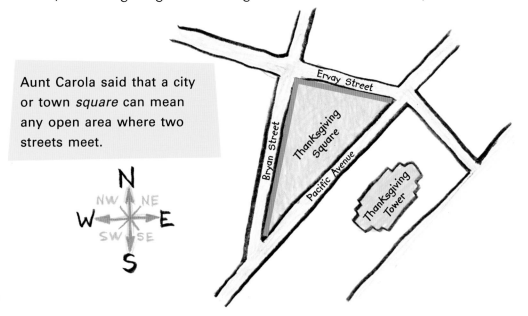

Once we were standing on the grass of Thanksgiving Square, the next direction on the paper told me to take a 360-degree turn. So I did, slowly spinning myself around in a complete circle so that I could look at everything surrounding the square. Aunt Carola said she saw a **vertex** (or the point where two sides of an angle meet) on the tall building in front of us and wanted to know whether I saw one, too. That was a tough one, but Aunt Carola sure does make exploring fun!

My 360-degree Turn

I saw a huge rectangular face—with a vertex at each corner—on the front of Thanksgiving Tower. I also saw the buildings around it reflected in its glass.

Geometry Note

right angle ⌐ an angle measuring 90 degrees

acute angle ∠ an angle measuring less than 90 degrees

vertex ∢ the point where two sides of an angle meet

11

The next direction on the paper said to "stand on the vertex of the right angle of Thanksgiving Square, look north down Bryan St., and then take a quarter turn to the left." One 90-degree turn later, we were walking down Ervay St. toward Ross Ave., where I needed to take another quarter turn to the left. I was so excited about following the directions that I got ahead of Aunt Carola and had to do a 180-degree turn—or half turn—to look back and see how far behind she was.

The sound of splashing water was everywhere, and we found ourselves at the bottom of a fountain whose small pools poured into one another like stair steps. Behind the waterfalls, huge jets of white water shot up into the air from holes in the ground. Behind that was the most amazing sight of all: a towering, blue, glass building, reflecting white clouds from the sky. It looked as if the building were one huge mirror!

Fountain Place has many edges where two faces touch each other.

This time it was my turn to point something out to Aunt Carola. "I see an **edge** between two faces," I said. She was very proud of me.

The Features of Fountain Place

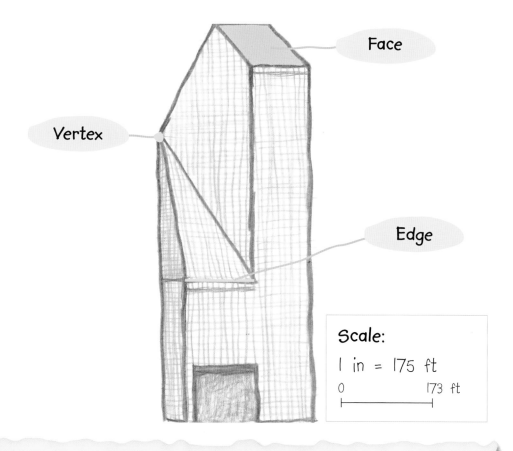

Face

Vertex

Edge

Scale:
1 in = 175 ft
0   173 ft

Geometry Note

edge 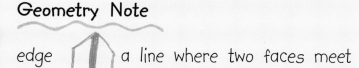 a line where two faces meet

13

The misty spray from the fountains cooled me down, yet I still felt hot . . . and hungry! I asked Aunt Carola if there were any good crab enchiladas around Dallas, afraid that she would say no. But Aunt Carola winked and said, "Follow me!" The restaurant we went to, unfortunately, didn't serve crab enchiladas, but it did serve shrimp tacos. As we ate, Aunt Carola warned me to save room for a very special dessert. I told her that this was almost as good as eating at Fisherman's Wharf but that I missed the seals.

With a smile, Aunt Carola told me that she'd show me some special Dallas animals that are much quieter than seals. After lunch and a short drive through downtown, I was staring at a whole herd of longhorn cattle. It's not surprising that these animals were quiet, for they were made of bronze!

Aunt Carola says that this sculpture celebrates the cattle trails that once ran through Dallas, even though more cattle were moved through Fort Worth. Still, it's the largest bronze sculpture in the world!

There's one Dallas building that I really wanted to see up close. It shines against the night skyline like a lit-up dandelion with starry lights instead of puffy seeds. I was really excited that Reunion Tower was the next stop on our tour.

It takes 14 miles of wires to keep the lights on Reunion Tower lit. Aunt Carola says that sometimes computers are programmed to make the lights flash in different patterns.

Aunt Carola and I zoomed up in an elevator to the top of the tower where there was another restaurant! This restaurant slowly turned 360 degrees, so we could see all of Dallas in 55 minutes without ever leaving our chairs.

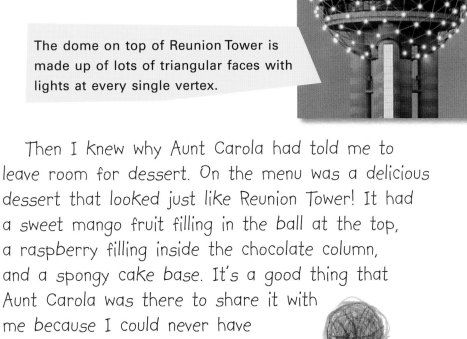

The dome on top of Reunion Tower is made up of lots of triangular faces with lights at every single vertex.

Then I knew why Aunt Carola had told me to leave room for dessert. On the menu was a delicious dessert that looked just like Reunion Tower! It had a sweet mango fruit filling in the ball at the top, a raspberry filling inside the chocolate column, and a spongy cake base. It's a good thing that Aunt Carola was there to share it with me because I could never have finished it by myself.

Friday, June 28

If I had wanted to, I could have slept late this morning. Instead, however, I got up early *because we were going to Fair Park to see museums, beautiful buildings, and a movie on a giant screen.* I couldn't wait for the adventure to begin!

As we walked past the huge Hall of State building off of Nimitz Dr., Aunt Carola did it again. "I see **perpendicular lines,** do you?" she asked.

Then she asked how I was enjoying my visit. Of course, I was having a great time and told her so. But then I had a question for her. I wanted to know whether she and Uncle Horacio would be staying in Dallas much longer. I really missed them and wanted them to move back to San Francisco.

I learned a lot about the Hall of State building from Aunt Carola. When I took this picture, however, I was more interested in the perpendicular lines I found.

As soon as the words came out of my mouth, I felt guilty. I hoped that she wouldn't be upset. What if she was unhappy here but couldn't move back because of Uncle Horacio's job? Had I just made things worse? I stared down at my feet and kicked my shoes against the ground, feeling my cheeks growing red.

Geometry Note

perpendicular lines   lines that intersect to form right angles

19

Neither of us said a word, but Aunt Carola led me to a pond where we sat. I watched some ducks paddle through the still water and the dragonflies that zipped around like red and blue sparks. I noticed that we were sitting on one part of an enormous reddish-orange sculpture with many long arms stretching across the water. It looked like an underwater octopus reaching in all directions for the shore.

Then Aunt Carola began talking about their move. She said that she and Uncle Horacio were sad to leave their family but that they were also very excited about the chance to explore a new place. What she said next made my heart sink. She said that they don't know whether they would ever live in San Francisco again.

I've had such fun with Aunt Carola and Uncle Horacio the past few days. It's really hard for me to accept that they'll stay here when I go back home to San Francisco. Still, I know there's nothing I can do to get them back to San Francisco any sooner—or at all!

Aunt Carola and I sat on this sculpture, which was built to help people get close enough to observe all the plants and animals in the pond.

Saturday, June 29

   This morning I was still so miserable about yesterday's talk that I didn't think I could have any more fun. I was so wrong! When I went into the kitchen for breakfast, there was something special sitting on my chair: three tickets to a Texas Rangers game at the Ballpark in Arlington. Uncle Horacio had gotten them for me as a surprise. He said that he knew my visit wouldn't be complete without a baseball game.

   I still couldn't believe that Aunt Carola and Uncle Horacio would never live near me again, but today I decided not to let that spoil the rest of my trip. If they can enjoy exploring new places, so can I.

This afternoon I could tell that Aunt Carola was glad that I was in a better mood. We walked all the way around the ballpark, talking about the shapes we saw and comparing this stadium to Pacific Bell Park in San Francisco. The Ballpark in Arlington isn't any better— or worse—just different.

The three of us had tons of fun trying to be the first one to spot a shape or an angle. Uncle Horacio surprised us both by saying, "I see something **symmetrical.** Can you find two halves that are exactly the same?"

Uncle Horacio was right that the front of the Ballpark in Arlington is symmetrical. Both sides of the front are the same size and shape.

Geometry Note

symmetrical having exactly the same shape and size

I didn't know why, but about halfway through the game, I really <u>did</u> start to feel better. Maybe it was the sound of everyone cheering all around me, or maybe it was Uncle Horacio and Aunt Carola laughing and arguing about which players were the best. Whatever it was, I was having a really good time.

Then I figured it out. If Aunt Carola and Uncle Horacio hadn't moved away, I might never have seen this ballpark . . . or eaten shrimp tacos . . . or traveled to the top of Reunion Tower. I wonder what other great new things Uncle Horacio and Aunt Carola will find while they live here. And if they move somewhere else, we can discover great new things in that place, too. I'm still not happy that they moved away from San Francisco, but at least I'm OK with it. I guess that's enough for now.

We had the most amazing seats at the game!

Sunday, June 30

I was very quiet on the way to the airport this morning, and Aunt Carola asked me what was wrong. I explained that I was thinking about how much I was going to miss her and Uncle Horacio. I added, however, that I understood why they liked Dallas. Then I promised to find some new things in San Francisco to show to them whenever they come back to visit us.

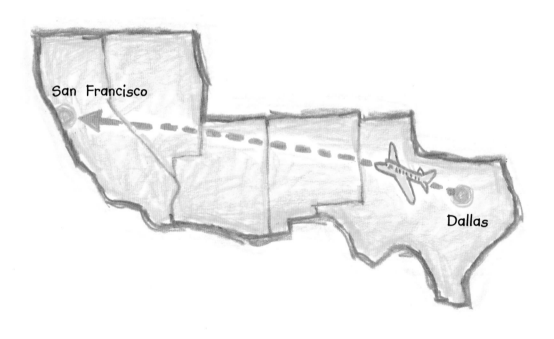

San Francisco

Dallas

Aunt Carola smiled and said that she would be looking forward to that, but I'd better hurry. It turns out that she and Uncle Horacio are coming back to San Francisco next month for Mom's birthday party! They want their visit to be a birthday surprise for Mom, so it will be hard not to show my excitement at home for the next few weeks. But I think I can keep the secret.

I now know that no matter how far away Aunt Carola and Uncle Horacio live, we'll always have a close relationship. I was afraid that we would change and that we wouldn't *be able* to share fun things together. But we haven't changed . . . or if we have, we've just found new things to share.

I think we should start sending each other pictures of things we see. If Aunt Carola finds an interesting new shape on a building, I want to be able to see it with her. And I've decided to send her copies of my photographs from this trip to show her what she helped me to see.

Who knows? Maybe some day Aunt Carola and Uncle Horacio will move to Mexico and send me pictures of Mayan pyramids! As long as I can see what they are seeing, maybe I won't miss them as much.

I'm sending copies of my photographs to Aunt Carola to show her some geometric features that I can see!

Arc

Acute Angle

Edge

Face

Obtuse Angle

Parallel Lines

Right Angle

Perpendicular Lines

Symmetrical

Vertex

Glossary

acute angle an angle measuring less than 90 degrees

arc a curved line that forms part of a circle

edge a line where two faces meet

face a flat side of a solid figure

obtuse angle an angle measuring more than 90 degrees but less than 180 degrees

parallel lines lines that do not cross and are always the same distance from each other

perpendicular lines lines that intersect to form right angles

right angle an angle measuring 90 degrees

symmetrical having exactly the same shape and size

vertex the point where two sides of an angle meet

Index